Cambridge Primary

Hodder Cambridge Primary

# Science

## Workbook

## Stage 6

Helen Lewis

Series editors: Rosemary Feasey
and Deborah Herridge

HODDER
EDUCATION
AN HACHETTE UK COMPANY

Acknowledgements

The Publisher is extremely grateful to the following schools for their comments and feedback during the development of this series:
Avalon Heights World Private School, Ajman
The Oxford School, Dubai
Al Amana Private School, Sharjah
British International School, Ajman
Wesgreen International School, Sharjah
As Seeb International School, Al Khoud

The publisher would like to thank the following for permission to reproduce copyright material.

**p.29** Reprinted from WHO releases country estimates on air pollution exposure and health impact. Nada Osseiran & Kimberly Chriscaden. Copyright World Health Organization (WHO) (2016). Accessed: 23 June 2017. URL: http://www.who.int/mediacentre/news/releases/2016/air-pollution-estimates/en/

Practice test exam-style questions are written by the author.

While every effort has been made to check the instructions for practical work described in this book carefully, schools should conduct their own risk assessments in accordance with local health and safety requirements.

Every effort has been made to trace all copyright holders, but if any have been inadvertently overlooked the Publishers will be pleased to make the necessary arrangements at the first opportunity.

Although every effort has been made to ensure that website addresses are correct at time of going to press, Hodder Education cannot be held responsible for the content of any website mentioned in this book. It is sometimes possible to find a relocated web page by typing in the address of the home page for a website in the URL window of your browser.

Hachette UK's policy is to use papers that are natural, renewable and recyclable products and made from wood grown in sustainable forests. The logging and manufacturing processes are expected to conform to the environmental regulations of the country of origin.

Orders: please contact Bookpoint Ltd, 130 Milton Park, Abingdon, Oxon OX14 4SB. Telephone: (44) 01235 827720. Fax: (44) 01235 400454. Lines are open from 9.00–5.00, Monday to Saturday, with a 24-hour message answering service. You can also order through our website www.hoddereducation.com

© Helen Lewis 2017

Published by Hodder Education

An Hachette UK Company

Carmelite House, 50 Victoria Embankment, London EC4Y 0DZ

Impression number    5 4 3

Year                            2019

Cover illustration © Steve Evans

Illustrations by Vian Oelofsen

Typeset in 12 on 14 pt FS Albert by IO Publishing CC

Printed in Great Britain by Hobbs the Printers Ltd, Totton, Hampshire SO40 3WX

A catalogue record for this title is available from the British Library

9781471884252

# Contents

# Unit 1 Humans and animals

## Body organs

**1** Write the name of each of these organs in the correct column of the table.

( heart )  ( nose )  ( kidneys )  ( intestines )

( stomach )  ( gallbladder )  ( brain )

( lungs )  ( skin )  ( ears )

| Internal organs | External organs |
| --- | --- |
| | |

**2** Choose an internal organ from question 1. Draw and label a diagram of it. Add a title. Write a caption to describe the function of the internal organ.

| Title: |
| --- |
| Labelled diagram: |
| |
| Caption: |

# Heart and circulation

 **1** Read the statements below about the heart. For each statement, circle True if the statement is true. Circle False if the statement is false.

| | Statement | Your answer | |
|---|---|---|---|
| a | Your heart is a muscle. | True | False |
| b | Your heart is in your chest, slightly to the right of the centre. | True | False |
| c | Your heart is about as big as your head. | True | False |
| d | Your heart is always beating. | True | False |
| e | Your heart pumps blood around your body in a three-stage process. | True | False |

**2** The diagram below shows the heart and circulatory system.

Label these parts of the diagram (one has been done for you):

( heart )    ( lungs )    ( artery )    ( vein )    ( rest of body )

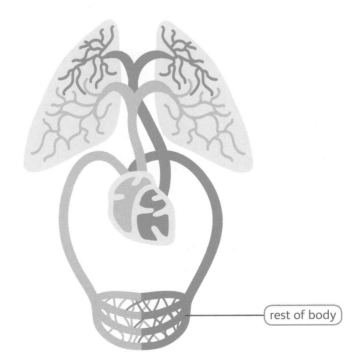

( rest of body )

 **3** How is your heart different to your other muscles? Describe two ways.

- _____

- _____

# Heart rate and exercise

 **1** Some Stage 6 learners measured their heart rates before and during exercise. They collected these two sets of data:

Zou     140
Nadia   115
Tyrone  125
Claudia 110
Lionel  120
Sergio  110

Zou     90
Nadia   80
Tyrone  85
Claudia 80
Lionel  75
Sergio  70

Which set of data do you think shows heart rate during exercise? Explain your reasoning.

_____

_____

 **2** **a** Use the two sets of data above to complete this table of results.

| Name | | | | | | |
|------|--|--|--|--|--|--|
| Heart rate before exercise | | | | | | |
| Heart rate during exercise | | | | | | |

**b** Who had the greatest difference between their heart rate before and during exercise?

_____

 **3** Explain why heart rate is higher during exercise.

_____

_____

_____

# Breathing

**1** Complete the table below about the process of breathing.
Use these words and phrases:

( carbon dioxide is breathed out )    ( move in )    ( fill up with air )

( flattens and moves downwards )    ( exhalation )

| Stage of breathing | What your diaphragm does | What your ribs do | What your lungs do | What happens inside your lungs |
|---|---|---|---|---|
| inhalation | | lift upwards and outwards | | oxygen passes into the bloodstream |
| | moves upwards | | air is pushed out of them | |

**2** **a** Draw and label a diagram to show what happens during inhalation.    **b** Draw and label a diagram to show what happens during exhalation.

# Animal brains

 **1** Look at the different brains. They belong to a human and various animals.

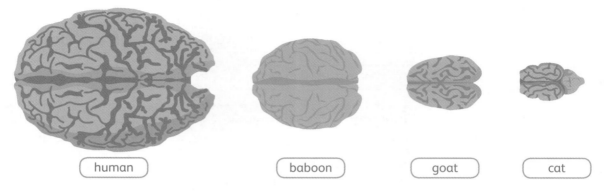

| human | baboon | goat | cat |

  **a** What similarities do you see between the different brains?

  _____

  **b** What differences do you see?

  _____

 **2** Some animals are surprisingly intelligent. For example, some animals:
  - use tools
  - mimic (copy) human speech
  - can be taught to communicate using sign language.

  Do some research to find out about one of these subjects.
  Write a short report about your findings.

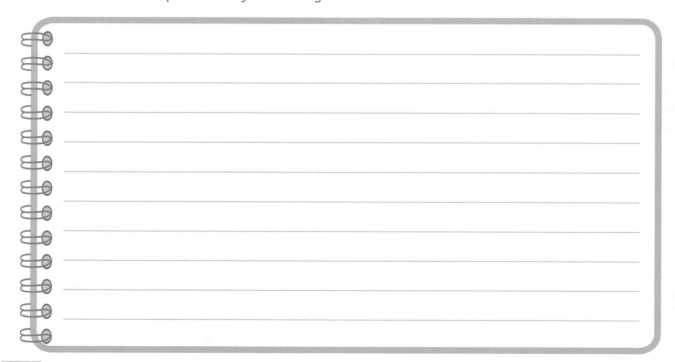

# Word search

**1** Find and circle these words in the word search grid below.

| reflex | cerebellum | cerebrum | nerves | inhalation | exhalation | diaphragm |

| trachea | arteries | capillaries | veins | cells | pulse | oxygen |

The words may be written in any of these directions:

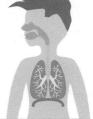

| S | C | T | R | A | C | H | E | A | O | P | A |
|---|---|---|---|---|---|---|---|---|---|---|---|
| E | D | C | N | V | E | R | E | F | X | M | R |
| I | I | E | O | E | R | P | U | E | Y | U | T |
| R | A | R | I | I | E | T | L | O | G | R | E |
| A | P | E | T | N | B | F | C | H | E | B | R |
| L | H | B | A | S | E | V | R | E | N | E | I |
| L | R | Y | L | R | L | P | B | R | U | R | E |
| I | A | G | A | P | L | L | U | T | E | E | S |
| P | G | E | H | H | U | O | E | L | I | C | N |
| A | M | N | N | R | M | X | A | C | S | E | R |
| C | N | O | I | T | A | L | A | H | X | E | L |

# Skin sensitivity

Some Stage 6 learners wanted to find out which areas of the body are the most sensitive to touch. They measured the shortest distance at which people could feel two points touching different areas of the body.

| Area of the body | Average shortest distance at which two points were felt (mm) |
|---|---|
| forehead | 15 |
| cheek | 6 |
| forearm | 35 |
| palm of hand | 10 |
| tip of index finger | 3 |

a Draw a bar chart to show the data in the table above. Remember to give your bar chart a title and label both axes.

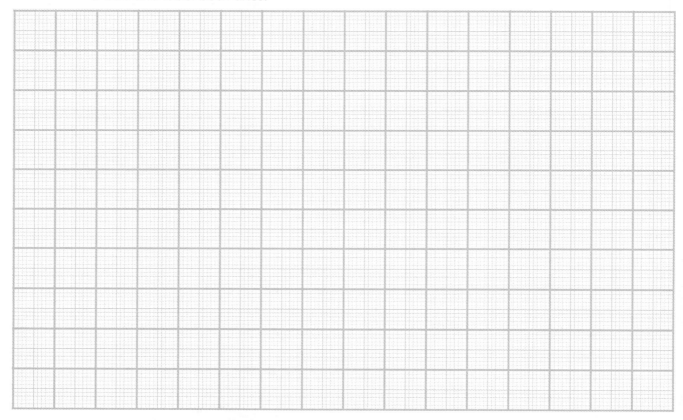

b What might happen if all areas of your body were as sensitive as the tip of the index finger?

_____

_____

# Modelling digestion

**1** The pictures below show five stages of digestion in a model.
Write a caption under each picture to describe what is happening.
Label each picture with the name of the object and what it represents (in brackets).
The first one has been done for you.

crackers and banana (food)

plastic bag (stomach)

Food enters the stomach.

**b**

**c**

**d**

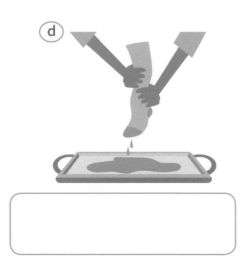

**e**

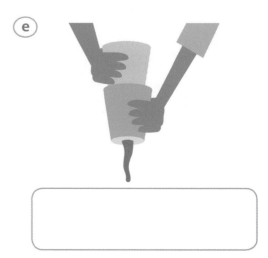

# The health benefits of exercise

Read the text below about some of the health benefits of exercise. Then answer the questions.

**Eight health benefits of exercise**

1 **Exercise strengthens your heart.** The heart is a muscle and it gets stronger with regular exercise. A strong heart protects against heart disease.

2 **Exercise strengthens your lungs.** It increases the amount of air your lungs can hold, and how effectively they move air in and out of your body. As a result, you take more oxygen into your body and you exhale more carbon dioxide. All the cells in your body benefit from this!

3 **Exercise strengthens your bones.** Your skeleton supports the rest of your body. It is important to have strong bones, especially when you are still growing.

4 **Exercise improves your energy levels.** Regular exercise makes you feel more energetic. It allows you to be more active, making you feel less tired during the day.

5 **Exercise helps you to sleep better.**

6 **Exercise helps you to concentrate better.**

7 **Exercise strengthens your immune system.** Your immune system is the body system that fights disease. A strong immune system means that your body is better able to fight infections such as colds and flu.

8 **Exercise helps you to feel happier.** Most people say that they feel calmer and have a greater sense of well-being after exercise.

a  What is the function of the immune system?
   Why is it good to have a strong immune system?

_____

_____

_____

b  Which other body systems does exercise benefit? Explain how you know.

_____

_____

_____

_____

c  Which of the eight benefits do you think are most likely to make you do more exercise? Why?

_____

_____

# A healthy diet

**1** Read these tips for a healthy diet.

Circle True if the tip is true. Circle False if the tip is false.

| | Healthy diet tip | Your answer | |
|---|---|---|---|
| **a** | Eat refined cereals (such as white bread and white rice) rather than wholegrain cereals (such as wholemeal bread and brown rice). | True | False |
| **b** | Drink plenty of water. | True | False |
| **c** | Eat at least five portions of fruit and vegetables a day. | True | False |
| **d** | Eat foods that are high in fat at every meal. | True | False |
| **e** | Eat foods that are high in sugar and salt only occasionally and in small amounts. | True | False |

**2** This menu is not very healthy.          Change the menu for a healthier option.

**Starter**
fried onion rings

**Main course**
fried chicken and fried potatoes

**Dessert**
ice cream sundae

**To drink**
cola

**Starter**

**Main course**

**Dessert**

**To drink**

# Body organs and systems quiz

**1** Tick one answer for each question.

**a** What is the name of the blood vessels that carry blood away from the heart?

◯ veins ◯ arteries ◯ capillaries ◯ intestines

**b** What is the scientific name for the windpipe?

◯ bronchi ◯ oesophagus ◯ trachea ◯ appendix

**c** Which part of your nervous system controls the automatic functions of your body?

◯ brain stem ◯ cerebellum ◯ cerebrum ◯ spinal cord

**d** Which of these is NOT a reflex?

◯ thinking ◯ blinking ◯ sneezing ◯ coughing

**e** On which area of your body is your sense of touch the most sensitive?

◯ cheek ◯ forearm ◯ fingertips ◯ palm of hand

**f** Which organ is the odd one out?

◯ oesophagus ◯ stomach ◯ small intestine ◯ spinal cord

**g** Which of these is NOT a characteristic of exercise?

◯ It makes your muscles work harder.

◯ It makes your breathe faster and deeper.

◯ It makes you feel cooler.

◯ It makes your heart beat more quickly.

**h** How much sleep does an 11 year-old child need every night?

◯ 10 hours ◯ 9.5 hours ◯ 9.25 hours ◯ 8.75 hours

# Self-assessment

## Unit 1 Humans and animals

| :) | I understand this well. |
| :| | I understand this but need more practice. |
| :( | I do not understand this yet. |

I need more help with …

_____

_____

_____

_____

| Learning objectives | :) | :| | :( |
|---|---|---|---|
| I can name the organs of the body using their scientific names. | | | |
| I can identify the position of the organs of the body. | | | |
| I can describe the functions of the organs of the body. | | | |
| I can explain why the organs of the body need to function properly. | | | |
| I can explain how the heart pumps blood around the body. | | | |
| I can design a model of the circulatory system. | | | |
| I understand how the respiratory system works. | | | |
| I can draw a cartoon to show how the nervous system works. | | | |
| I know the names of the three main parts of the brain. | | | |
| I can investigate how good my sense of touch is. | | | |
| I understand the process of digestion. | | | |
| I know that we need the right amount of sleep to function properly. | | | |
| I have researched the work of a famous scientist. | | | |

# Unit 2 Food chains

## Mountain habitat

**1** Circle the organisms that live in a mountain habitat.

You may need to do some research.

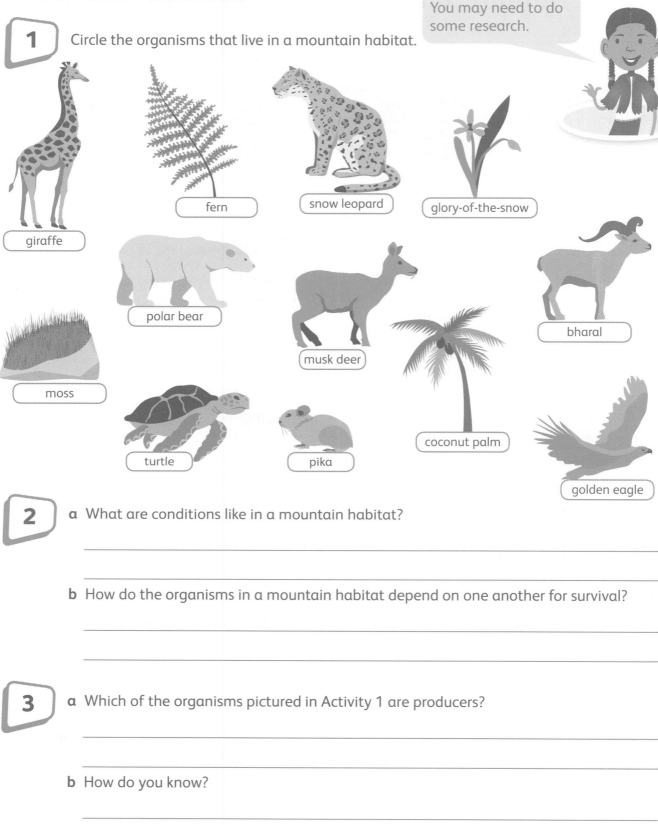

giraffe

fern

snow leopard

glory-of-the-snow

polar bear

bharal

moss

musk deer

coconut palm

turtle

pika

golden eagle

**2** **a** What are conditions like in a mountain habitat?

_____

_____

**b** How do the organisms in a mountain habitat depend on one another for survival?

_____

_____

**3** **a** Which of the organisms pictured in Activity 1 are producers?

_____

_____

**b** How do you know?

_____

_____

# Mountain food chains

pika – eats moss

**1** The pictures below show a few of the plants and animals that live in the Himalayan Mountains in Asia.

snow leopard – eats bharal and musk deer

moss

glory-of-the-snow

musk deer – eats glory-of-the-snow

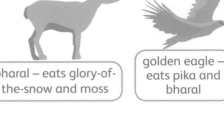

bharal – eats glory-of-the-snow and moss

golden eagle – eats pika and bharal

Use the information to create five food chains. One has been done for you as an example.

(a)

(b)

(c)

(d)

(e)

# Word puzzle

**1** Rearrange each set of letters to make scientific words from Unit 2.
Then write the words in the grid below. The first one has been done for you.

If you have written all the words correctly, another scientific word from Unit 2 will appear in the shaded squares.

1 deadpat _____adapted_____   2 ratpored _____

3 magsrosin _____   4 notidoncis _____

5 tentsruin _____   6 dofo anchi (two words) _____ _____

7 erpy _____   8 airnefrsots _____

9 unmessorc _____

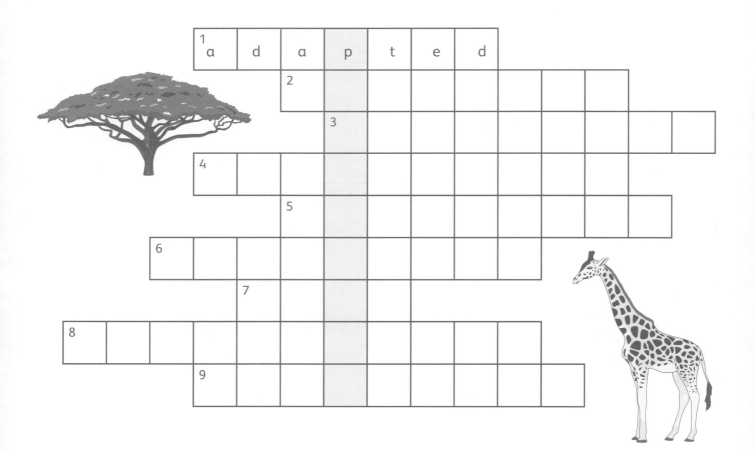

# Predator adaptations

 **1** The cheetah is a predator. Add labels to the picture to show the adaptations the cheetah has that help it to hunt.

**2** These pictures show some hunting techniques.

_____    _____

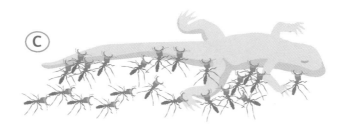

_____

**a** Label each picture above with the name of the hunting technique. Choose from:

( ambush )    ( pack hunting )    ( trapping )

**b** Choose one of the hunting techniques. Explain how it helps the predator to catch its prey.

_____

_____

_____

# More adaptations

Here is a list of adaptations.

( eyes on the side of the head )   ( camouflage )   ( pack hunting )

( living in groups )   ( body built for speed )   ( ambush )

( eyes at the front of the head )   ( sharp teeth )

**1** Write each adaptation above in the correct column of this table.

| Body adaptations | Behaviour adaptations |
|---|---|
|  |  |
|  |  |
|  |  |

**2** Write each adaptation from the list at the top of the page in the correct part of this diagram.

( predator adaptations )                    ( prey adaptations )

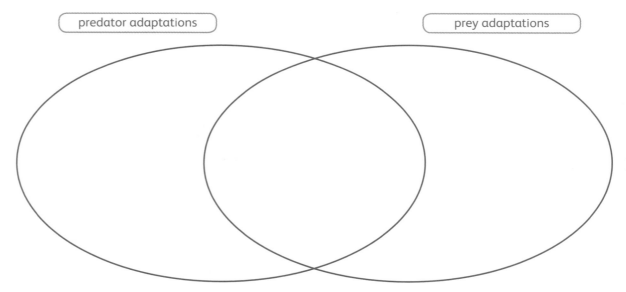

**3** **a** Name one more predator or prey adaptation.

_____

**b** Write this adaptation in the correct column of the table in Activity 1.

**c** Write this adaptation in the correct part of the diagram in Activity 2.

# A seashore food web

**1** In the space below, name some of the plants and animals that live in a seashore habitat. Make notes about their feeding relationships.

You will need to do some research.

**2** Draw a food web to show the feeding relationships from Activity 1.

# Food chain predictions

 **1** Predict what might happen to the organisms in the food chain when there is a change in the habitat. Explain your prediction.

a

| Food chain | Change |
|---|---|
| leaf → caterpillar → frog → snake | Warm, wet weather speeds up plant growth, and leads to more leaves than usual. |
| **Prediction** | **Explanation** |
| | |

b

| Food chain | Change |
|---|---|
| fig → tapir → boa constrictor → harpy eagle | A disease that affects fig trees leads to fewer figs. |
| **Prediction** | **Explanation** |
| | |

c

| Food chain | Change |
|---|---|
| phytoplankton → shrimp → bluefish → swordfish | Humans catch all the swordfish. |
| **Prediction** | **Explanation** |
| | |

# Risk assessment

Choose a habitat near your school to visit. Fill in this risk assessment table.

Use the information to help to make sure that your visit is safe.

| Activity | Hazard | Possible accident | What we can do to prevent it |
|---|---|---|---|
|  |  |  |  |
|  |  |  |  |
|  |  |  |  |
|  |  |  |  |
|  |  |  |  |
|  |  |  |  |

# What have you learnt about food chains?

**1** Write a definition for each of these words.

**a** producer

_____

**b** consumer

_____

**c** predator

_____

**d** prey

_____

**2** The organisms below come from different habitats.
Draw arrows to make four food chains.
Use a different colour for the arrows in each food chain.

ladybird

spider

shark

aphids

garden plants

monkey

lion

zebra

jaguar

jellyfish

avocado

shrimp

acacia tree

phytoplankton

# Self-assessment

## Unit 2  Food chains

☺ I understand this well.

😐 I understand this but need more practice.

☹ I do not understand this yet.

I need more help with …

_____

_____

_____

_____

| Learning objectives | ☺ | 😐 | ☹ |
|---|---|---|---|
| I can name different habitats and describe what they are like. | | | |
| I know that plants use energy from the Sun to make their own food. | | | |
| I know that every food chain begins with a plant that is called the producer. | | | |
| I can explain what a consumer is in a food chain. | | | |
| I know that food chains represent the feeding relationships in a habitat. | | | |
| I can draw and label food chains in different habitats, including a tropical rainforest, the ocean and a savanna. | | | |
| I can explain the words 'predator' and 'prey'. | | | |
| I can explain how some predators' bodies are adapted to help them to hunt. | | | |
| I can explain how some prey animals are adapted to help them to avoid being eaten. | | | |
| I know that a food web is made up of several food chains linked together. | | | |
| I have investigated food chains in a local habitat. | | | |

## Endangered species fact files

**1**

**a** Choose two animal species that are endangered.
You could choose two from these, or another two:

( mountain gorilla )   ( blue whale )   ( snow leopard )

( black rhino )   ( red panda )   ( orangutan )

**b** Fill in a fact file about each endangered animal. Do some research to help you.

**c** Draw or stick a picture of the animal onto the fact file.

Common name:

Scientific name:

Habitat(s):

Diet:

Average life span:      Size:

Weight:      Number in the wild:

Threats:

Common name:

Scientific name:

Habitat(s):

Diet:

Average life span:      Size:

Weight:      Number in the wild:

Threats:

# Deforestation information leaflet

 Use the space below to create an information leaflet. Tell people about the causes and effects of deforestation. Use some of these words in your leaflet:

| deforestation | causes | farming | population | logging |

| effects | soil erosion | climate change | rainforests | biodiversity |

# Waste survey

Some Stage 6 learners carried out a waste survey at their school.
Here are the results of the survey.

| Survey questions | Answers |
|---|---|
| How many classrooms have a paper recycling bin? | 10 out of 10 |
| Does every classroom collect junk materials for modelling? | Yes |
| Does the school have a compost bin for fruit and vegetable waste? | No |
| Does the school encourage learners to use refillable drink bottles? | Yes |
| How many litter bins are there in the playground? | 1 |
| Do the playground litter bins divide litter into recyclable and non-recyclable items? | No |
| Does the school have a policy of mending broken items whenever possible? | Yes |
| Does the school encourage learners to bring only unpackaged snacks to school? | No |

 **1** Write an email to the head teacher of the school. Suggest actions that the school could take to improve the way it manages waste.

| New Message | — ⤢ X |
|---|---|
| **To** | Cc  Bcc |
| **Subject** | |

Send

# Air pollution

 **1** Read this article about air pollution. Then answer the questions below.

**Air pollution – a global health problem**

Across the world, air pollution causes around 3.3 million deaths every year – most of them in Asia. A recent study points towards that number doubling by the year 2050.

Two air pollutants are most closely linked to ill health. They are particulates (tiny particles that are less than a thousandth of a millimetre across) and nitrogen dioxide (a gas).

Particulates and nitrogen dioxide are linked to serious diseases and long-term health problems, including lung cancer and heart disease.

The sources of air pollution that have the largest impact on health are different in different parts of the world. For example, the main sources of particulates and nitrogen oxide:

- in India and China, are fuels burned in the home for heating and cooking

- in most parts of the United States, are road traffic and power generation.

- in Europe, are farming activities.

a About how many deaths every year is air pollution expected to cause

by the year 2050? _____

b Which are the air pollutants most closely linked to ill health?

_____

_____

c For people living in India and China, which sources of air pollution have the largest impact on health?

_____

d Find out about sources of air pollution where you live. Write a short report on what you find out.

_____

_____

_____

_____

# Climate change mind map

**1** Create a mind map to show what you know about climate change. Here are some words and phrases you could use.

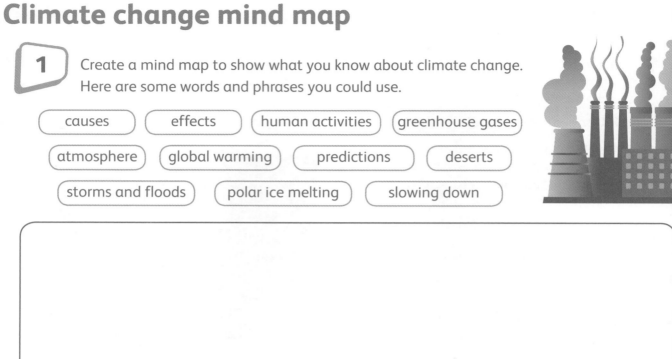

( causes )  ( effects )  ( human activities )  ( greenhouse gases )

( atmosphere )  ( global warming )  ( predictions )  ( deserts )

( storms and floods )  ( polar ice melting )  ( slowing down )

climate change

# Sort that waste!

**1** Into which bin should you put each waste item?
Write the name of each waste item on the correct bin.

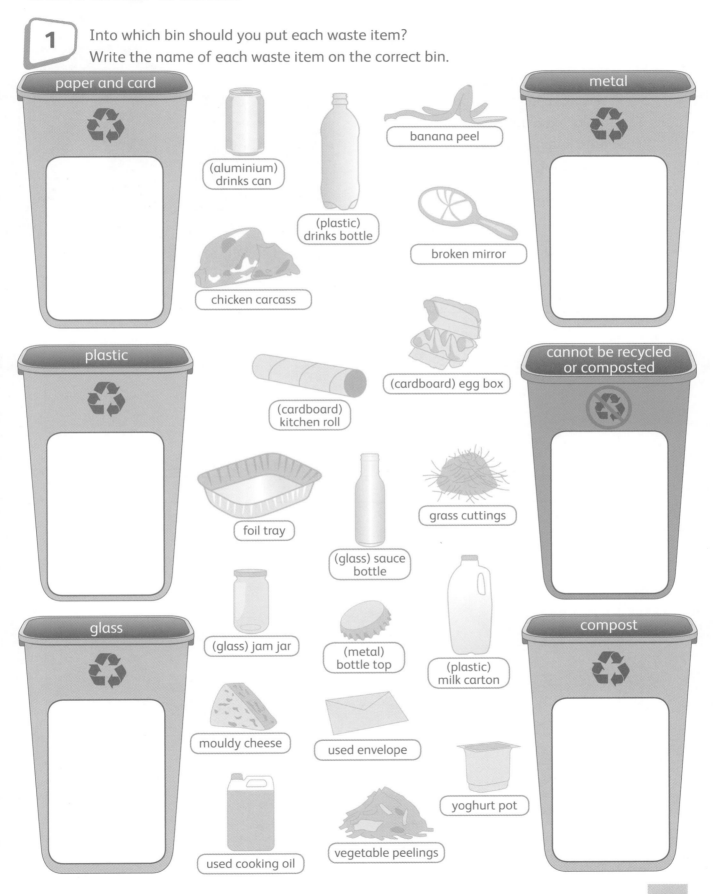

paper and card

metal

plastic

cannot be recycled or composted

glass

compost

(aluminium) drinks can

banana peel

(plastic) drinks bottle

broken mirror

chicken carcass

(cardboard) egg box

(cardboard) kitchen roll

foil tray

grass cuttings

(glass) sauce bottle

(glass) jam jar

(metal) bottle top

(plastic) milk carton

mouldy cheese

used envelope

yoghurt pot

used cooking oil

vegetable peelings

# Mend it!

To help to keep waste levels down we can reduce, reuse and recycle waste. Write a set of instructions for mending a damaged item.

For example, you could write instructions for:

- sewing a patch on a pair of jeans
- replacing a button
- patching a punctured bicycle tyre
- something else.

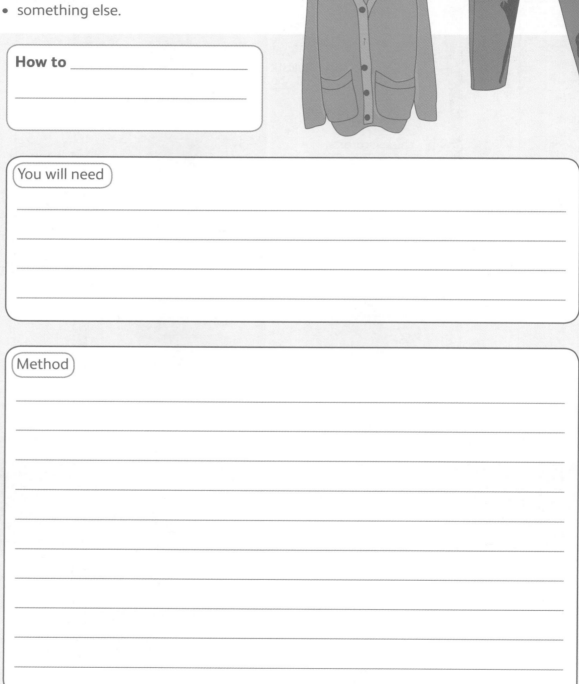

**How to** _____

_____

You will need

_____

_____

_____

_____

Method

_____

_____

_____

_____

_____

_____

_____

_____

_____

_____

# Renewable energy sources

**1**

The pictures on this page show some renewable energy sources.

**a** Write a title next to each picture. Choose from these words:

( bio energy )   ( hydroelectric energy )   ( solar energy )   ( wind energy )

**b** Write a caption underneath each picture to explain:
- what it is
- its good points
- how it works
- its bad points.

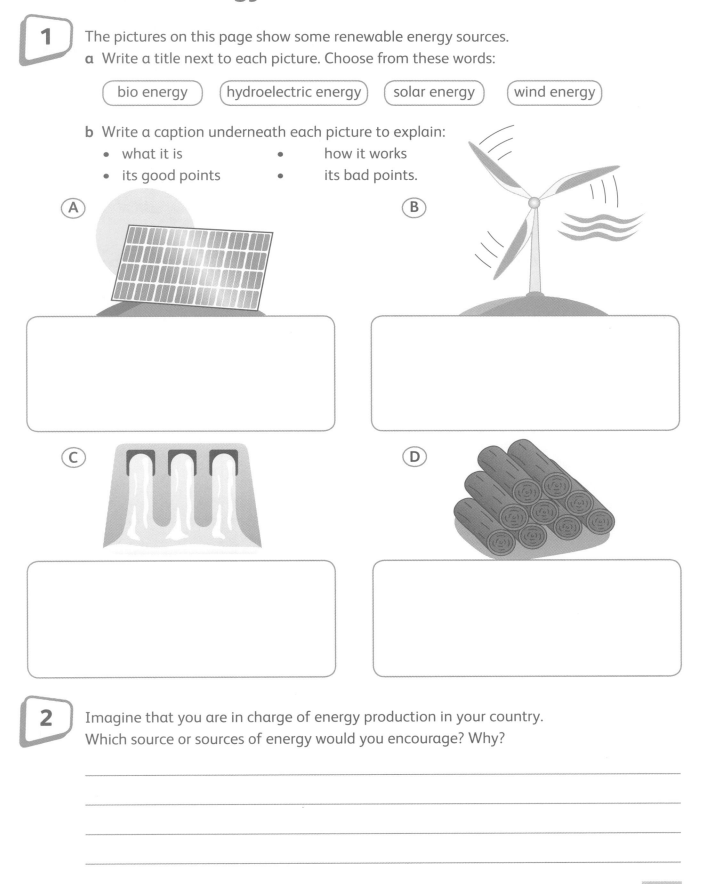

Ⓐ

Ⓑ

Ⓒ

Ⓓ

**2**

Imagine that you are in charge of energy production in your country. Which source or sources of energy would you encourage? Why?

_____

_____

_____

_____

# Saving energy

Some Stage 6 learners are planning a 'low-energy use day'.
They have made a list of all the classroom appliances that use mains electricity.

**a** Decide if each appliance needs to be on all the time or not.

**b** For the appliances that do not need to be on all the time, suggest what the learners could do to use less electricity on 'low-energy use day'.

| Classroom appliances that use mains electricity | Does it need to be on all the time? If so, why? | If the appliance does not need to be on all the time, what could you do to use less electricity, other than not using it? |
|---|---|---|
| computers | | |
| interactive whiteboard | | |
| fish tank pump and heater | | |
| fire alarm | | |
| air conditioning system | | |
| lights | | |

# Do not litter! poster

 **1** Design and make a poster to display this message clearly: Do not litter!
Use at least four key scientific words on your poster.

DO NOT LITTER!

# Self-assessment

## Unit 3  Caring for the environment

🙂 I understand this well.

😐 I understand this but need more practice.

🙁 I do not understand this yet.

I need more help with …

_____

_____

_____

_____

| Learning objectives | 🙂 | 😐 | 🙁 |
|---|---|---|---|
| I can explain what is meant by the term 'the environment'. | | | |
| I know that some plants and animals have become endangered or extinct because humans have destroyed their habitats. | | | |
| I understand that waste materials can have a damaging effect on the environment. | | | |
| I know why polluted water can poison plants and animals. | | | |
| I know why air pollution can be harmful to humans and the environment. | | | |
| I can explain what is meant by 'global warming' and 'climate change'. | | | |
| I can describe different ways of caring for the environment, for example, by reducing waste and recycling. | | | |
| I know what is meant by 'renewable' energy and can name some renewable energy sources. | | | |
| I can suggest ways to save energy. | | | |
| I know what conservationists do to help to protect habitats. | | | |
| I can suggest ways that I can help to care for the environment, for example, by not dropping litter. | | | |

# Unit 4 Material changes

## Explaining changes

**1** Hamid is confused about changes of state.

Condensation, evaporation, freezing, melting?
I do not understand.

**a** Explain to Hamid what each word means.

| condensation | evaporation |
|---|---|
|  |  |
| freezing | melting |
|  |  |

**b** Give Hamid an example of each change of state.

condensation _____

evaporation _____

freezing _____

melting _____

**c** Complete the diagram to show Hamid how the four changes of state are related to the three states of matter.

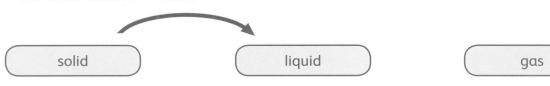

solid        liquid        gas

# Reversible and irreversible changes

**1**  **a** Draw and label a diagram to show a reversible change.

Do not forget to label your diagrams to make them really clear.

**b** Draw and label a diagram to show an irreversible change.

**2** Look at the diagrams you drew in Activity 1. Decide which of the materials you could change back again. Draw and label a diagram to show how you would do it.

# Investigating melting

 **1** Some Stage 6 learners carried out an investigation to find out how quickly ice would melt in different locations around their school. They left a block of ice to melt.
Every two minutes they took the block of ice and measured its mass.

Here is their table of results.

| Location | Mass of ice at beginning of test | Mass of ice after 2 minutes | Mass of ice after 4 minutes | Mass of ice after 6 minutes | Mass of ice after 8 minutes |
|---|---|---|---|---|---|
| A | 16 g | 12.5 g | 9 g | 5.5 g | 2 g |
| B | 16 g | 12 g | 8 g | 4 g | 0 g |
| C | 16 g | 13.5 g | 11 g | 8.5 g | 6 g |
| D | 16 g | 13 g | 10 g | 7 g | 4 g |

Plot the data from the table in a line graph. Use a different colour to show the data for each location. One set of data, for location A, has been plotted for you.

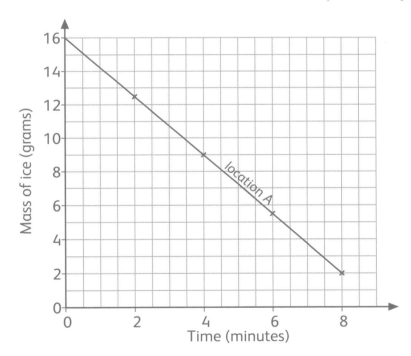

 **2** a Order the locations according to their temperature, from highest to lowest.

_____

b Explain how you know which location had the highest temperature.

_____

_____

# Material changes crossword

 Use the clues given below to complete this crossword.

**Across**

2  This sort of change has taken place if a material can be changed back to the way it was before.

6  The process in which a material changes state from a gas to a liquid.

7  What everything you see around you is made of.

8  The process in which a liquid changes state to become a solid.

9  The opposite of 8 across.

**Down**

1  The opposite of 2 across.

3  A puddle drying up is an example of this change of state.

4  The temperature at which a solid melts is called its melting _____.

5  A liquid does this when evaporation takes place all the way through the liquid, not just on the surface.

# Fire!

 **1**   For burning to take place, what three things must be present?

- _____

- _____

- _____

 **2**   The pictures below show three ways to put out a fire.

**Hint:** Think about the answers you gave to question **a**.

putting a fire blanket over the fire

**a**  How does this method put out the fire?

_____

pouring water on the fire

spraying carbon dioxide on the fire

**b**  How does this method put out the fire?

_____

_____

**c**  How does this method put out the fire?

_____

_____

 **3**   Which method of putting out a fire would you NOT use on electrical equipment? Why?

_____

_____

# Investigating rusting

 **1** Some Stage 6 learners wanted to find out the answer to this question:

Which liquid will cause an iron nail to rust the fastest: apple juice, cola, orange juice, vinegar or water?

The learners set up a test to find out the answer to this question.

| apple juice | cola | orange juice | vinegar | water |

Predict which liquid will cause an iron nail to rust the fastest. Explain your thinking.

_____

_____

_____

_____

_____

 **2** The Stage 6 learners left the nails in the liquids for a week. Then they removed the nails from the liquids and observed them. Here are their observations:

**Apple juice:**
The nail has some rust on it.
**Cola:**
The nail has turned black, but there is no rust.
**Orange juice and vinegar:**
The nail is unchanged.
**Water:**
The nail is covered in rust.

Do the observations that the learners made support the prediction you made in question 1? If not, how are they different? Suggest an explanation for any differences.

_____

_____

_____

_____

# Making butter

 A group of Stage 6 learners made some butter.

They poured 240 ml cream into a clean jar and screwed on the lid.
Then they shook the jar continuously.

After shaking the cream for several minutes, the learners heard a splashing sound.
When they looked at the jar they saw a solid yellow lump (butter) and a white liquid (buttermilk).

The learners measured the mass of butter and the volume of buttermilk.
They found that 240 ml cream produced 100 g of butter and 100 ml of buttermilk.

What type of change did the cream undergo – reversible or irreversible?
Explain your thinking.

_____

_____

 Use the data the learners collected to predict the volume of cream you would need:

**a** to make 50 g butter

_____

**b** to make 250 g butter

_____

**c** to make 200 ml buttermilk

_____

**d** to make 300 ml buttermilk

_____

# Changes in cooking

Complete this table about changes in cooking.

| Change | What causes the change? (heating, mixing, both, or something else) | Is the change reversible or irreversible? | How do you know if the change is reversible or irreversible? |
|---|---|---|---|
| **a** freezing orange juice to make ice lollies | | | |
| **b** toasting marshmallows | | | |
| **c** frying an egg | | | |
| **d** melting cheese | | | |
| **e** baking biscuits | | | |
| **f** browning onions | | | |
| **g** putting butter in the refrigerator to firm up | | | |

# A new material

**1**   **a** Imagine that you are a materials chemist who has made a new material.
What are the special properties of your new material?
Choose three properties from these words:

( does not rust )   ( light (in mass) )   ( strong )   ( flexible (bendy) )   ( elastic (stretchy) )

( conducts electricity well/does not conduct electricity )   ( hard (does not scratch easily) )

( produces lots of friction/produces very little friction )   ( reflects light well/does not reflect light )

( burns easily/does not burn easily )   ( conducts heat well/does not conduct heat )

- _____
- _____
- _____

**b** List three uses that the new material might have.
**Hint:** Think about its special properties.

- _____
- _____
- _____

**c** Why would the material be suitable for each of the uses you listed in question **b**?

- _____
  _____
- _____
  _____
- _____
  _____

**d** What would you call the new material? Why?

_____
_____
_____

# Separating mixtures of materials

**1** Write a set of instructions for separating the mixture of materials in this jar.

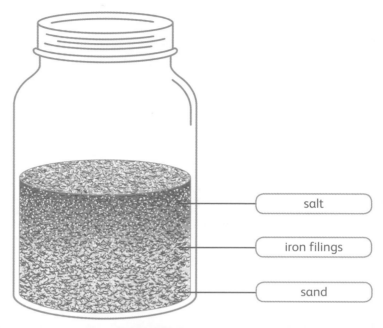

salt

iron filings

sand

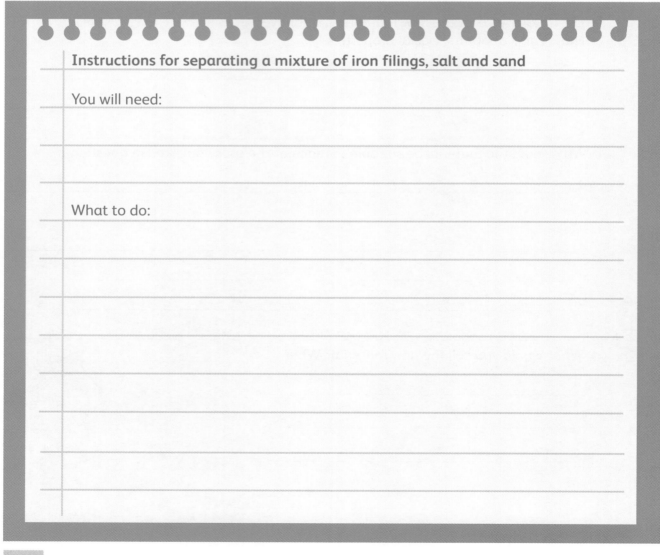

**Instructions for separating a mixture of iron filings, salt and sand**

You will need:

What to do:

# Dissolving sugar

**1** Some Stage 6 learners carried out an investigation to find out how much sugar would dissolve in 300 ml of water at different temperatures.

Here is their table of results.

| Temperature of water | 20 °C | 40 °C | 60 °C | 80 °C | 100 °C |
|---|---|---|---|---|---|
| Mass of sugar that dissolved in 300 ml of water | 240 g | 300 g | 360 g | 420 g | 480 g |

Plot a line graph of the data in the table on the graph paper below.

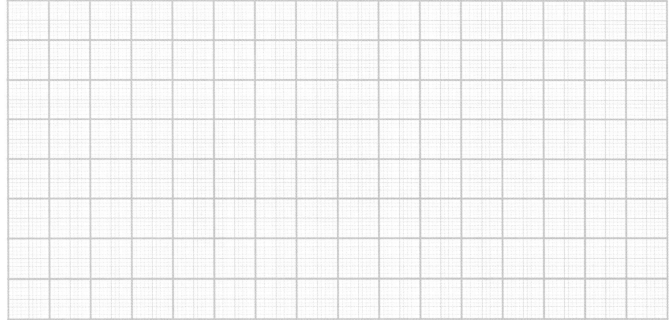

**2** Use the line graph to predict the mass of sugar that would dissolve in 300 ml of water at a temperature of:

a 30 °C _____  b 50 °C _____  c 90 °C _____

**3** What conclusion can you draw from the results of the investigation?

_____

_____

# Drinking water

**a** Research how drinking water is produced where you live. Find out six facts.

**b** Write the facts in the shapes around the picture.

# Show what you know about material changes

 **1** Complete each line of the phrase **material changes** with a word or phrase that has something to do with material changes.

Two letters have been done for you.

Look back over what you have done in this unit to help you!

**M** 

**A** filter

**T** 

**E** 

**R** 

**I** 

**A** 

**L** 

**C** 

**H** 

**A** 

**N** 

**G** 

**E** 

**S** tates of matter

# Material changes cartoon

 Create a cartoon to explain what you have learned about material changes to learners in another class. Draw your cartoon in the boxes.

You will need to decide which facts to include, how to present them as a cartoon, and the best order for them.

# Self-assessment

## Unit 4  Material changes

☺ I understand this well.

😐 I understand this but need more practice.

☹ I do not understand this yet.

I need more help with …

_____

_____

_____

_____

| Learning objectives | ☺ | 😐 | ☹ |
|---|---|---|---|
| I can recognise and name the processes of condensation, evaporation, melting and freezing. | | | |
| I can explain the difference between a reversible change and an irreversible change. | | | |
| I can name some reversible and irreversible changes. | | | |
| I can say what conditions are needed for the changes of burning and rusting to take place. | | | |
| I know that some materials change when they are mixed together. | | | |
| I can follow a recipe and describe the changes that take place when foods are mixed together or cooked. | | | |
| I have researched the work of materials chemists to find out which new materials they have invented. | | | |
| I can explain how to separate mixtures of solids. | | | |
| I can observe, describe and begin to explain what changes happen when I add some solids to water. | | | |
| I can use a filter to separate some solids and liquids. | | | |
| I know that some solids dissolve in water to form a solution – the solid cannot be seen but it is still there. | | | |

# Unit 5 Forces and motion

## Forces

 **1** Look at these pictures, which show forces in action.
Draw an arrow on each picture to show the direction of the named force.
Write next to the arrow whether the force is a **push** or a **pull**.

(a)

the force of gravity acting on the feather

(b)

the force the child is applying to the go-kart

(c)

the force the wind is applying to the sail

(d)

the magnetic force acting on the iron filings

 **2** Which do you think is the strongest force in the pictures? Explain your thinking.

_____

_____

# Mass and weight

**1** Answer these questions about mass and weight.

   **a** Which is the downward force exerted by an object that is being pulled by gravity: mass or weight?

   _____

   **b** Which is a measure of the amount of matter an object contains: mass or weight?

   _____

   **c** In what unit is weight measured?

   _____

   **d** In what unit is mass measured?

   _____

   **e** True or false: If one object has more mass than another, it also weighs more.

   _____

   **f** A mass of 1 kilogram weighs about how many newtons?

   _____

**2** On Earth, an astronaut has a mass of 90 kilograms and a weight of 900 newtons. Now imagine the same astronaut floating in space, far away from the pull of Earth's gravity.

   **a** What is the astronaut's mass in space? Explain your thinking.

   _____

   _____

   _____

   _____

   _____

   **b** What is the astronaut's weight in space? Explain your thinking.

   _____

   _____

   _____

   _____

# Leaving the Moon

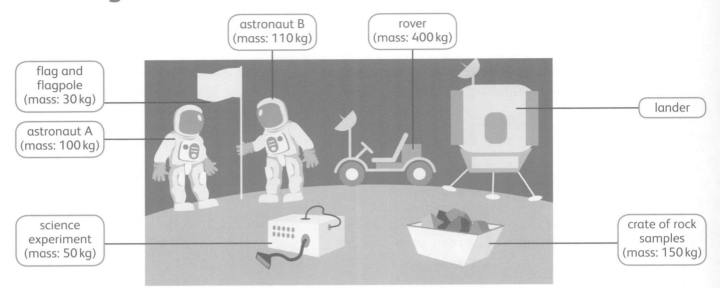

astronaut B
(mass: 110 kg)

rover
(mass: 400 kg)

flag and
flagpole
(mass: 30 kg)

lander

astronaut A
(mass: 100 kg)

science
experiment
(mass: 50 kg)

crate of rock
samples
(mass: 150 kg)

**1** It is time for the astronauts to leave the Moon in the lander. First, they need to find out if the lander has enough fuel to carry all the objects they brought with them.

**a** The lander has 200 litres of fuel left. It will use one litre of fuel for every three newtons it carries back to the spacecraft. What is the maximum weight the lander can carry back to the spacecraft? _____N

**b** Help the astronauts to work out the weight of each person and object on the Moon by completing the table below. The first row has been done for you.

weight (N) = mass (kg) × strength of gravity (N/kg)

| Person/Object | Mass (kg) | Strength of gravity on the Moon (N/kg) | Weight of object on the Moon (N) |
|---|---|---|---|
| astronaut A | 100 kg | 1.6 N/kg | 160 N |
| astronaut B | | 1.6 N/kg | |
| rover | | 1.6 N/kg | |
| crate of rock samples | | 1.6 N/kg | |
| science experiment | | 1.6 N/kg | |
| flag and flagpole | | 1.6 N/kg | |
| **Total weight on the Moon** | | | |

**c** Does the lander have enough fuel to carry everything back to the spacecraft? _____

**d** If you answered 'No' to question **c**, which objects should the astronauts leave on the Moon? Explain your thinking.

_____

_____

_____

_____

# Weight in water

**1** Some Stage 6 learners collected six objects that do not float in water.
They used a force meter to weigh each object in air and then in water.
Here is the data they collected.

**Weight in air:**
object A 25N, object D 10N, object F 34N,
object B 19N, object C 9N, object E 28N

**Weight in water:**
object D 3N, object C 2N, object A 5N,
object F 9N, object E 7N, object B 4N

**a** Use the data above to complete this table of results.

| Object | A | B | C | D | E | F |
|---|---|---|---|---|---|---|
| Weight in air (N) | | | | | | |
| Weight in water (N) | | | | | | |

**b** Use the table of results to draw a bar chart. Draw two bars for each object.

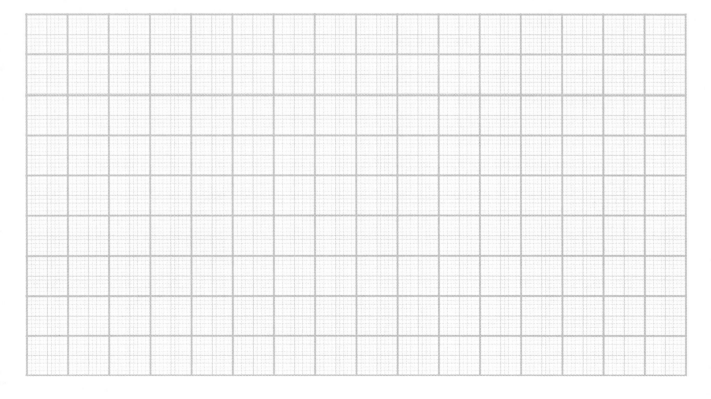

# Balanced and unbalanced forces

**1** Some of the diagrams below show balanced forces. Some show unbalanced forces. The force acting on each object affects the way it moves.

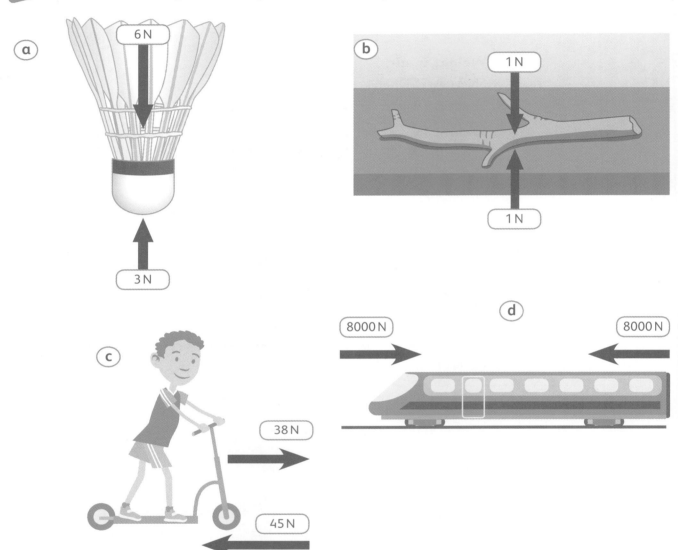

Write the letter of each force diagram (a, b, c and d) in the correct part of this table.

| Motion | Forces | |
|---|---|---|
| | Balanced forces | Unbalanced forces |
| not moving | | |
| constant speed | | |
| speeding up | | |
| slowing down | | |

# Making craters

 **1**  Some Stage 6 learners wanted to find out which ball would make a larger crater. They dropped two balls into damp sand.

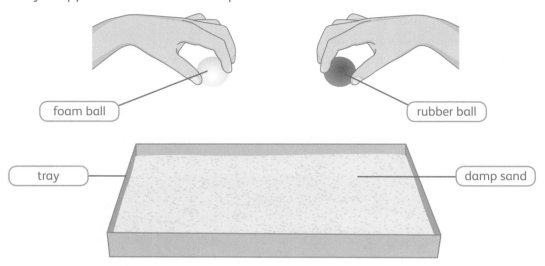

foam ball

rubber ball

tray

damp sand

**a**  Predict which ball will make the larger crater.

_____

**b**  Explain the answer you gave in question **a**.

_____

_____

 **2**  The learners carried out the test. Here is their table of results.

| Material of ball | Diameter of crater (mm) | | |
|---|---|---|---|
| | Test 1 | Test 2 | Test 3 |
| rubber | 64 | 63 | 68 |
| foam | 45 | 49 | 42 |

**a**  Predict the size of the crater made by the ball in this picture. Will it be larger or smaller than the rubber ball?

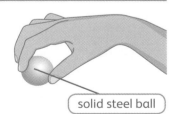

solid steel ball

_____

**b**  Why do you think that? Use the table of results in your explanation.

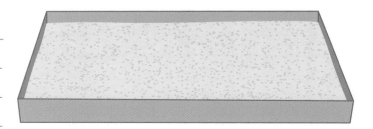

_____

_____

_____

_____

# Levers

**1** Below are some objects that use levers.
For each object:

- Write what it is used for.
- Draw arrows to show the force applied.
- Draw arrows to show the force produced.

The first object has been done for you.

(a)

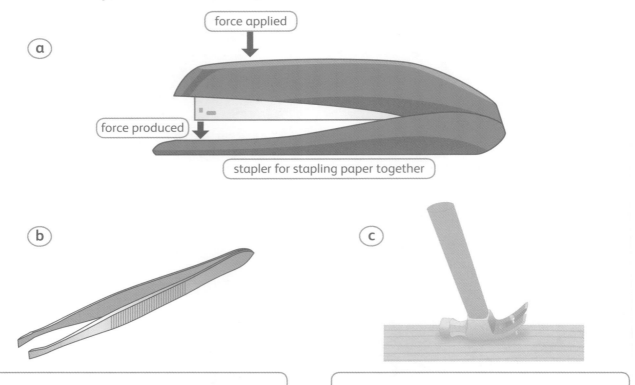

force applied

force produced

stapler for stapling paper together

(b)

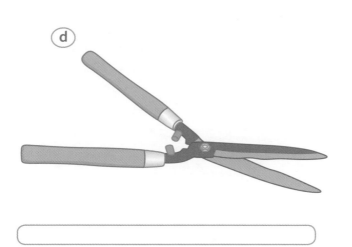

(c)

(d)

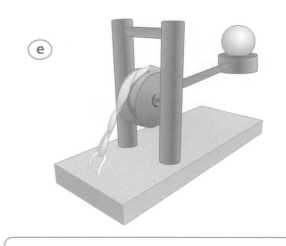

(e)

# Inclined planes

**1**  Some Stage 6 learners carried out an investigation to find out if the angle of an inclined plane affects how much force is needed to move a load up the slope.

 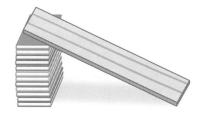

**a**  Here is their table of results. Calculate the average values.

| Angle between the inclined plane and the floor | Length of inclined plane needed to raise the load to the height of the books | Force needed to move the load up the incline (N) | | | |
|---|---|---|---|---|---|
| | | Test 1 | Test 2 | Test 3 | Average |
| 10° | 180 cm | 11 | 12 | 7 | |
| 20° | 155 cm | 9 | 14 | 13 | |
| 30° | 130 cm | 12 | 14 | 16 | |
| 40° | 105 cm | 19 | 16 | 16 | |
| 50° | 80 cm | 24 | 23 | 22 | |

**b**  Write the missing words in this sentence. Choose from:

( more )   ( less )

The greater the angle between the inclined plane and the floor:

• the _____ the length of inclined plane needed to raise the load to a given height.

• the _____ force is needed to move a given load up the incline.

**2**  The Singh family are moving house. They need to lift their piano into the removals van. They have decided to use an inclined plane. They have a choice of three planks for making the inclined plane.

Ⓐ    Ⓑ

Ⓒ

Which plank should the Singh family use to make their inclined plane? Why?

_____

_____

# Wheels and axles

**1** Find three objects or pictures of objects that use wheels and axles. Draw a sketch of each object in one of the rectangles. Draw a close-up sketch of one of the object's wheels and axles in the circle next to it. Label your sketches.

# What I know about simple machines

**1** Show what you know about the different types of simple machines below.
You could:

- Write sentences.
- Draw a labelled diagram.
- Use a combination of these.

**levers**

**inclined planes**

**wheels and axles**

**gears**

# Friction: helpful or a problem?

**1** Look at the pictures and answer the questions.

a

high friction between a car's tyres and the road

Is high friction in this situation helpful
or a problem? _____

Why? _____

_____

_____

_____

b

the tyres on this car are bald

Why are bald tyres a problem for the driver?

_____

_____

What should the driver do about it?

_____

_____

c

low friction between the skater's skates and the ice

Is low friction in this situation helpful
or a problem? _____

Why? _____

_____

_____

_____

d

low friction between the girl's socks and the polished floor

Is low friction in this situation helpful
or a problem? _____

Why? _____

_____

_____

_____

# Air resistance

**1** These three cars have the same mass. They have identical wheels and an identical engine. They all travel the same distance at the same speed.

car A

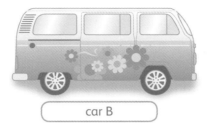

car B

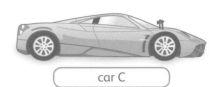

car C

a  Which car do you think will use the least fuel during the journey? _____

b  Explain the answer you gave to question **a**. Use these scientific words:

surface area     air resistance     direction

_____

_____

_____

**2** Look at these positions a skydiver can take.

position A          position B          position C

a  In which position do you think the skydiver will fall the slowest? _____

b  Explain the answer you gave to question **a**. Use these scientific words:

surface area     air resistance     direction

_____

_____

_____

# How does it work?

**1** Use what you know about forces and motion to explain how each of these objects works. Use some of these words:

| lever | force | load | inclined plane |

| gears | wheels | axles | turning force |

You could draw force diagrams to help you.

ⓐ see-saw

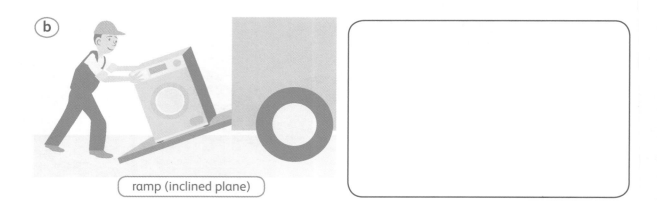

ⓑ ramp (inclined plane)

ⓒ bicycle

# Self-assessment

## Unit 5 Forces and motion

| | |
|---|---|
| :) | I understand this well. |
| :\| | I understand this but need more practice. |
| :( | I do not understand this yet. |

I need more help with …

_____

_____

_____

_____

| Learning objectives | :) | :\| | :( |
|---|---|---|---|
| I know what a force is and can show the direction in which a force is acting. | | | |
| I can measure a force in newtons using a force meter. | | | |
| I can explain the difference between mass (measured in kilograms) and weight (measured in newtons). | | | |
| I know that friction is a force that acts in the opposite direction to movement. | | | |
| I can describe how friction, including air resistance and water resistance, affects the way objects move. | | | |
| I can show how pairs of forces act on a force diagram. | | | |
| I can explain what balanced and unbalanced forces are. | | | |
| I know that all moving objects have the energy of movement. | | | |
| I can show how forces work in simple machines such as levers and gears. | | | |
| I have investigated how friction affects the speed at which objects move. | | | |
| I have discovered how the work of scientists in the past has helped our understanding of forces and motion. | | | |

# Electricity mind map

**1** Create a mind map to show what you know about electricity. Here are some words you could use:

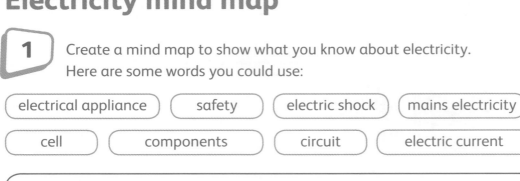

( electrical appliance )   ( safety )   ( electric shock )   ( mains electricity )

( cell )   ( components )   ( circuit )   ( electric current )   ( switch )

electricity

Keep adding to this mind map throughout the unit. When you learn something new, use different-coloured pencils or pens.

# Circuits

**1** Write instructions for making a circuit that will make a buzzer sound.
Include a picture of the circuit. Label each component.

**2** Ashira made a circuit with two cells, a lamp and a switch.
When Ashira tested the circuit the lamp did not light.

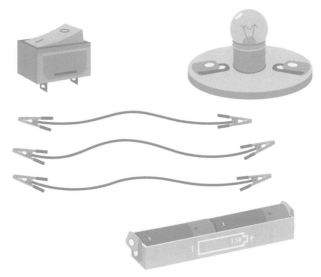

Give three possible reasons why the lamp did not light.

- _____
- _____
- _____

# Circuit diagrams

 **1** Look at these circuit diagrams.
List the components in each circuit. The first one has been done for you.

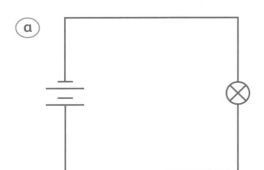

ⓐ

Components:
two wires, two cells, one lamp

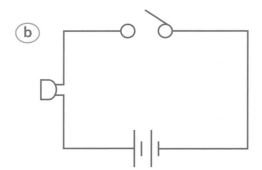

ⓑ

Components:

_____

_____

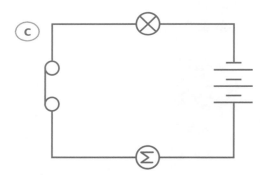

ⓒ

Components:

_____

_____

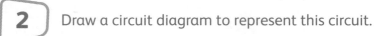

**2** Draw a circuit diagram to represent this circuit.

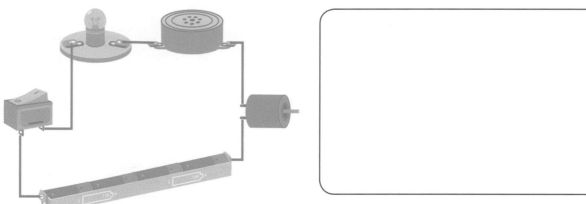

# Electrical cells

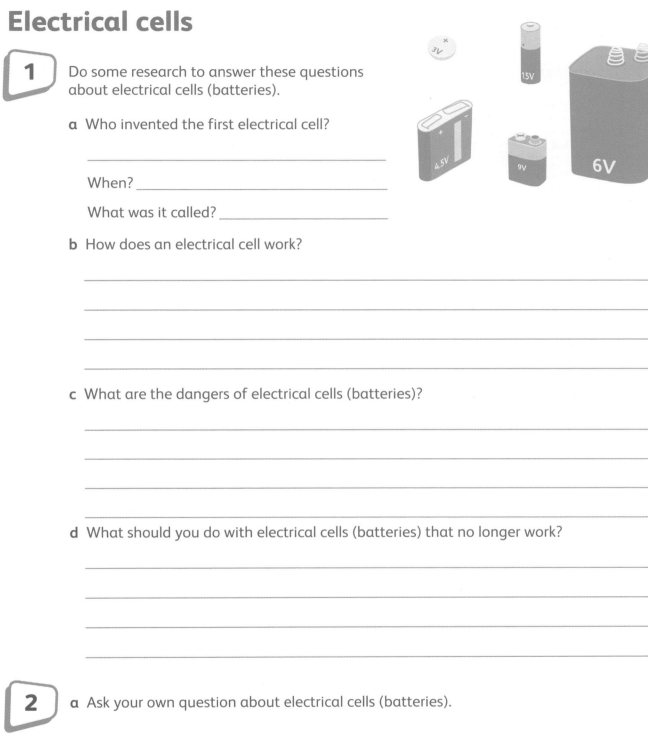

**1** Do some research to answer these questions about electrical cells (batteries).

a Who invented the first electrical cell?

_____

When? _____

What was it called? _____

b How does an electrical cell work?

_____

_____

_____

_____

c What are the dangers of electrical cells (batteries)?

_____

_____

_____

_____

d What should you do with electrical cells (batteries) that no longer work?

_____

_____

_____

_____

**2** a Ask your own question about electrical cells (batteries).

_____

_____

b Now answer your question.

_____

_____

# Bridging the gap

**1** Some Stage 6 learners collected these objects:

( copper pipe )   ( woollen jumper )   ( brass doorknob )   ( nickel coin )

( sticky note )   ( brick )   ( cardboard box )   ( silver chain )

They built this circuit:
They used each object in turn
to bridge the gap in the circuit.

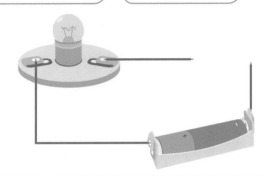

Here is their table of results.

| Object | Material | Result: Did the lamp light? |
|---|---|---|
| pipe | copper | yes |
| jumper | wool | no |
| doorknob | brass | yes |
| coin | nickel | yes |
| sticky note | paper | no |
| brick | brick | no |
| box | cardboard | no |
| chain | silver | yes |

**a** Does electric current flow equally well through all materials?

_____

**b** Explain how you know the answer to question **a**.

_____

_____

_____

**c** Think about the kinds of materials that allow electric current to flow through them well.
What do these materials have in common?

_____

**d** Choose a material that the learners did not test. Predict if it will allow electric current
to flow through it. Explain your thinking.

_____

_____

# Conductors and insulators

  **a** Explain what an electrical conductor is.

_____

_____

**b** Name four materials that are electrical conductors.

_____  _____

_____  _____

**c** Explain what an electrical insulator is.

_____

_____

**d** Name four materials that are electrical insulators.

_____  _____

_____  _____

  What sort of material (conductor or insulator) is used for:
**a** overhead power lines?

_____

**b** the handle of the powerline worker's tool?

_____

**c** the powerline worker's gloves?

_____

# Finding out more

 **1** What would you like to find out about electrical conductors and insulators?
Write three questions. Use some of these question starters or use your own ideas.

| Which material...? | Who made...? | What is a...? |
| How do...? | Where...? | Why...? |

a _____

_____

b _____

_____

c _____

_____

**2** Do some research to answer your questions from question 1.

Look for information written especially for children.

Make sure that the information you collect is about electrical conductors and insulators.

a _____

_____

_____

_____

b _____

_____

_____

_____

c _____

_____

_____

_____

# Long wires, short wires

 **1** Some Stage 6 learners carried out an investigation to find out if the length of wires in a circuit affects the electric current flowing through it. Here is their table of results. (Electric current is measured in units called amps.)

| Length of wire (cm) | Electric current (amps) | | | |
|---|---|---|---|---|
| | Test 1 | Test 2 | Test 3 | Average |
| 4 | 1.30 | 1.75 | 1.45 | 1.50 |
| 8 | 0.85 | 0.90 | 1.10 | 0.95 |
| 12 | 0.55 | 0.80 | 0.75 | 0.70 |
| 16 | 0.40 | 0.45 | 0.65 | 0.50 |
| 20 | 0.40 | 0.35 | 0.60 | 0.45 |
| 24 | 0.45 | 0.35 | 0.40 | 0.40 |

Draw a line graph to show the average values from the table.

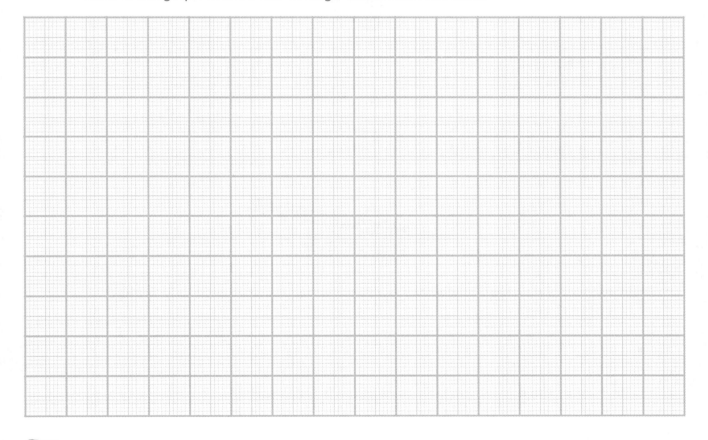

 **2** What conclusion can you draw from the data?

_____

_____

# Changing voltage

  **a** What is voltage?

_____

Jed changes this circuit:

into this circuit:

**b** How will the changes that Jed has made to the circuit affect the brightness
of the lamp?

_____

_____

**c** Explain the answer you gave to question **b**. Use the word volts.

_____

_____

**d** How could Jed change the circuit to make the lamp brighter than it was at first?
Write two ways.

• _____

• _____

# Circuit quiz

**1**　**a** Read this definition of a circuit. Write the missing word on the line.

A **circuit** is a complete loop, with no _____, around which electricity can flow.

**b** What is the general name given to electrical devices connected together in a circuit?

_____

**c** What does this circuit symbol represent?

_____

**d** What is wrong with this circuit diagram?

_____

_____

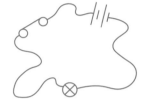

**e** What is wrong with this circuit diagram?

_____

_____

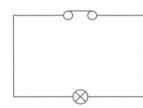

**2**　Write your own quiz questions about circuits.

**a** _____

_____

**b** _____

_____

**c** _____

_____

**d** _____

_____

**e** _____

_____

**3**　Give the questions you wrote in question 2 to a partner to answer.

How many questions did your partner answer correctly?

# Series circuits and parallel circuits

 **1** Which circuits below are series circuits? Which are parallel circuits?
Write 'series' or 'parallel' underneath each circuit diagram.

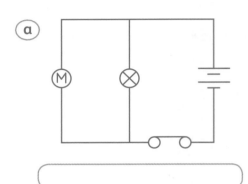

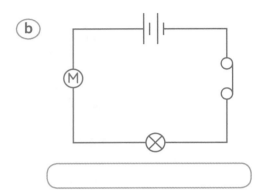

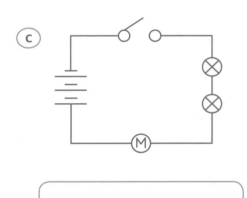

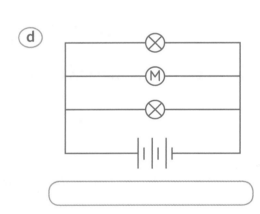

**2** This is a parallel circuit.

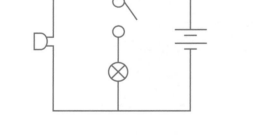

Draw a circuit diagram that shows the same components in a series circuit.

**3** Look at the diagram of a parallel circuit and your drawing of a series circuit in question 2. When might you choose to use a parallel circuit rather than a series circuit?

_____

_____

# Harry's switches

 Harry has made a model house with a light in every room.

This diagram shows the circuit in the model house.

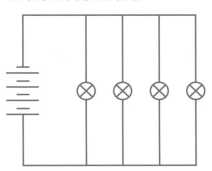

**a** Harry wants to be able to switch each light in the house on and off separately. Draw a cross on the diagram above to show where he should put each switch.

**b** Harry also wants to be able to switch all the lights in the house on and off at the same time. Draw a circle on the diagram above to show where he should put the switch to do this.

**c** Harry does not have any switches. He only has these materials:

Write a set of instructions for Harry. Explain how to make a switch. Include a labelled diagram.

paper fasteners

paperclip

scissors

sheet of card

# Electrical word search

Find and circle these words in the grid below:

| conductor | insulator | parallel | series | circuit |
| electricity | voltage | volts | Franklin | Volta |

The words may be written in any of these directions:

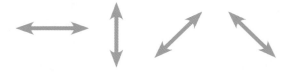

| C | I | R | C | U | I | T | A | R | T | U | I |
|---|---|---|---|---|---|---|---|---|---|---|---|
| H | E | O | O | B | E | S | Q | I | R | Y | S |
| G | C | I | N | S | U | L | A | T | O | R | S |
| H | V | I | D | C | P | L | C | H | B | E | G |
| E | O | A | U | K | A | F | P | K | R | A | N |
| E | L | E | C | T | R | I | C | I | T | Y | I |
| N | T | H | T | O | A | A | E | O | O | A | L |
| F | A | D | O | I | L | S | T | A | J | A | K |
| T | G | P | R | G | L | B | L | L | G | P | N |
| A | E | E | M | F | E | T | D | D | O | L | A |
| L | O | J | S | T | L | O | V | O | E | V | R |
| L | E | T | I | M | E | S | K | G | S | V | F |

# Electrical jokes

 **1**   Here are some electrical jokes. Choose the correct answer for each joke:

( electri-city )   ( shock-o-lot )   ( a Volts-wagen )

 a      What is an electrician's favourite ice cream flavour?

_____

 b   What kind of car does an electrician drive?

_____

b      Which is the smallest city?

_____

 **2**   Write your own electrical joke in the speech bubble.
Give your joke to a partner. Can they guess the answer?

# Self-assessment

## Unit 6 Electricity

| 😊 | I understand this well. |
| 😐 | I understand this but need more practice. |
| 😞 | I do not understand this yet. |

I need more help with …

_____

_____

_____

_____

| Learning objectives | 😊 | 😐 | 😞 |
|---|---|---|---|
| I can draw a diagram of an electrical circuit using circuit symbols. | | | |
| I understand that the electric current flows through the wire to the different components in an electrical circuit. | | | |
| I have investigated which materials are good conductors of electricity. | | | |
| I know that some materials are better conductors of electricity than others. | | | |
| I can explain why metals are used for electric cables. | | | |
| I can explain why plastic is used to cover wires, plugs and switches. | | | |
| I know what happens to a circuit if you change the length or thickness of the wire. | | | |
| I can explain how the voltage of the cell (battery) affects the components in a circuit. | | | |
| I have designed and made an electric-powered model. | | | |
| I can make a parallel circuit and connect components in separate loops. | | | |
| I have found out how a famous scientist has contributed to what we now know about electricity. | | | |